MW00824160

LEVEL SEVEN

PIANO REPERTOIRE

SELECTED & EDITED BY

Keith Snell

Etudes

THE NEIL A. KJOS PIANO LIBRARY

The **Neil A. Kjos Piano Library** is a comprehensive series of piano music in a wide variety of musical styles. The library is divided into eleven levels and will provide students with a complete performance experience in both solo and ensemble music. Teachers will find the carefully graded levels appropriate when choosing repertoire for evaluations, auditions, festivals, and examinations. Included in the **Neil A. Kjos Piano Library:**

Preparatory Level - Level Ten

Fundamentals of Piano Theory
Piano Repertoire: Baroque & Classical
Piano Repertoire: Romantic & 20th Century
Piano Repertoire: Etudes
Scale Skills
Essential Piano Repertoire
Music of the 21st Century
New Age Piano
Jazz Piano
One Piano Four Hands
Music for Christmas

PREFACE

Piano Repertoire: Etudes from the **Neil A. Kjos Piano Library** offers piano students graded studies for the development of technic, style and musicianship. Used in conjunction with *Baroque & Classical* and *Romantic & 20th Century*, *Etudes* provides pianists with additional music by composers of the 17th - 20th centuries in an assortment of styles, each piece precisely selected to reinforce the technical requirements found in the corresponding collections. The carefully graded levels ensure steady and thorough progress as pianists advance in their study of etudes.

Compact disc recordings are available for each volume in the *Piano Repertoire* series. Recorded by pianist Diane Hidy, the interpretations follow the editions closely as practical examples for students. Each CD includes all three volumes from the *Piano Repertoire* series at each level: *Baroque & Classical*, *Romantic & 20th Century*, and *Etudes*.*

*Preparatory and Level One are included on one CD.

CONTENTS

ISBN 0-8497-6237-5

Etude I

Carl Czerny
(1791-1857)

Allegro

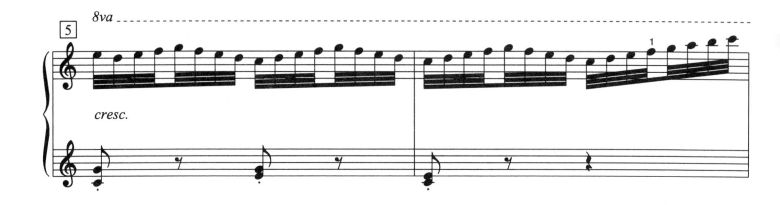

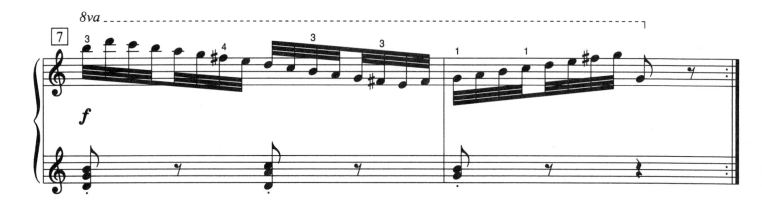

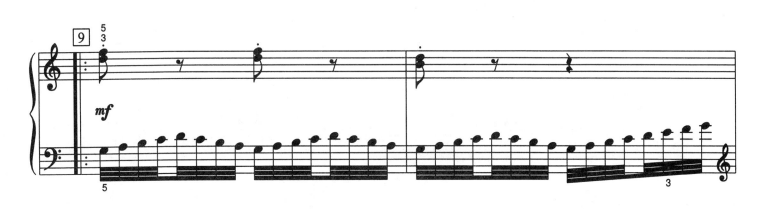

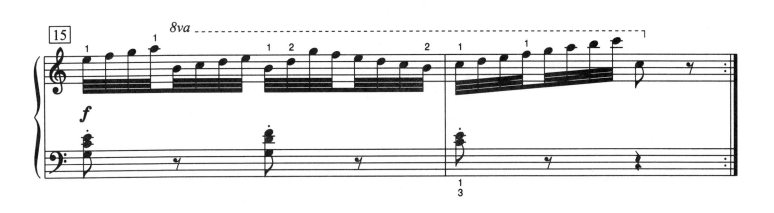

Etude II

Carl Czerny
(1791-1857)

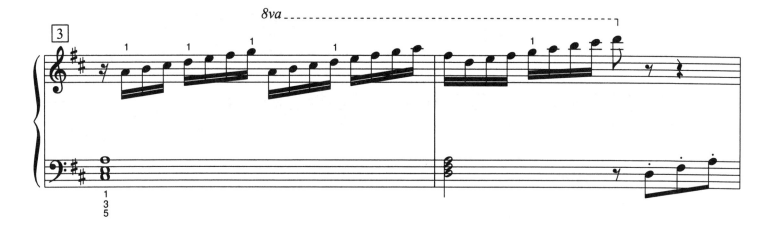

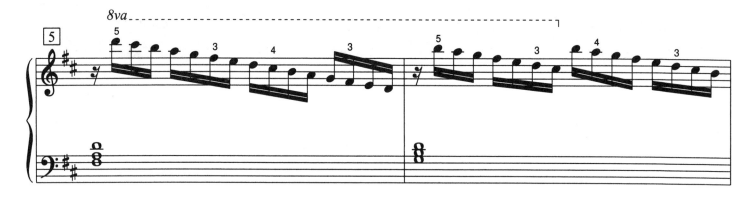

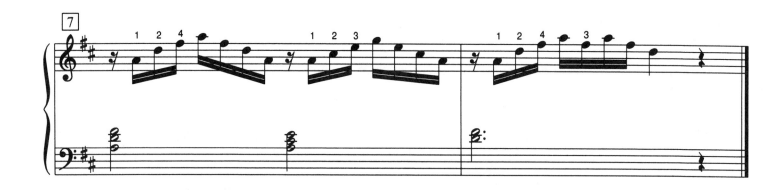

Legato Thirds

Giuseppe Concone
(1801-1861)

© 1997 Neil A. Kjos Music Company, 4380 Jutland Drive, San Diego, California, 92117.

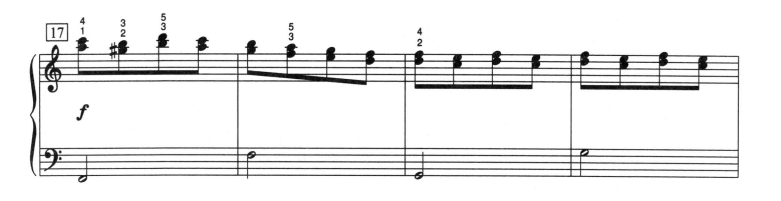

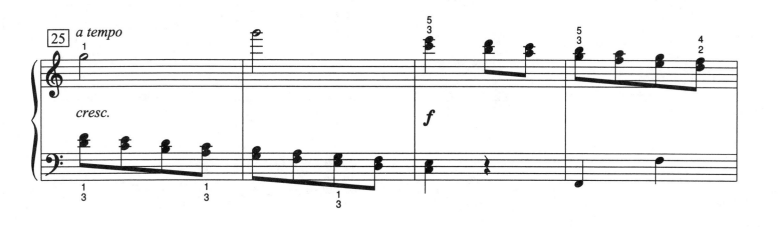

Velocity

Op. 109, No. 10

Friedrich Burgmüller
(1806-1874)

Etude

Op. 46, No. 1

Stephen Heller
(1814-1888)

Through Wind and Rain

Op. 45, No. 23

Stephen Heller
(1814-1888)

Allegro di molto

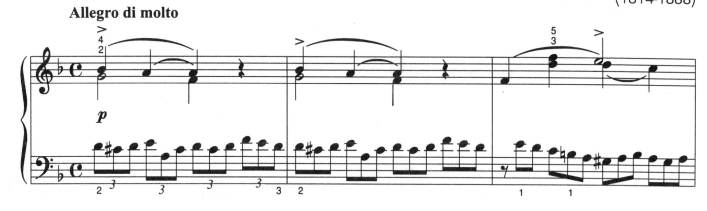

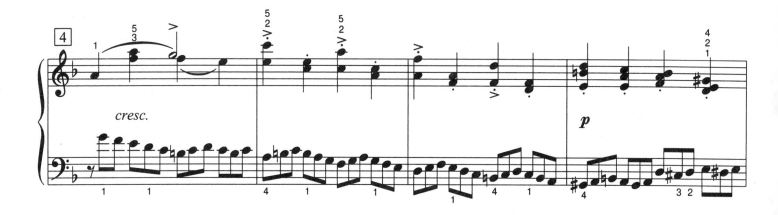

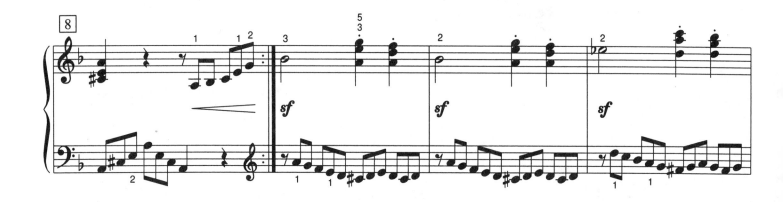

Ballade

Op. 46, No. 23

Stephen Heller
(1814-1888)

Allegro non troppo

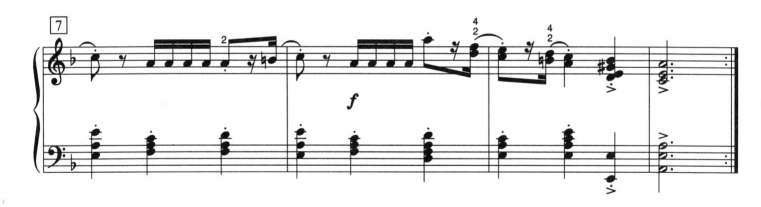

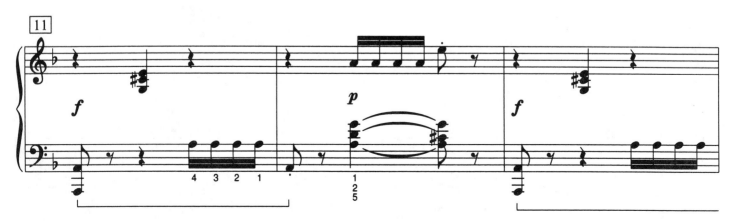

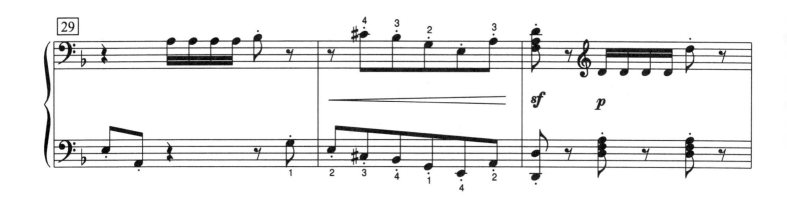

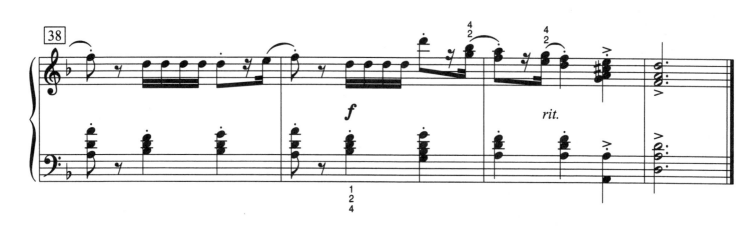

The Storm

Op. 46, No. 18

Stephen Heller
(1814-1888)

20

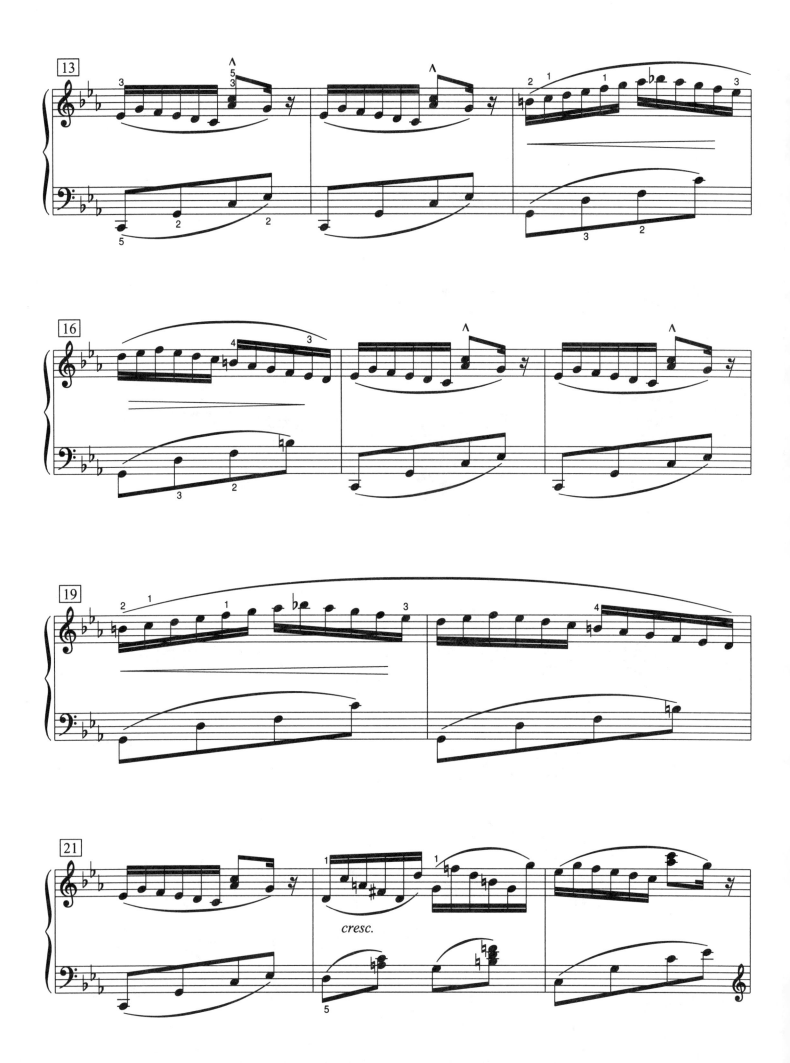

Over Hill and Dale

Op. 45, No. 24

Stephen Heller
(1814-1888)

Romance

Op. 39, No. 3

Edward MacDowell
(1860-1908)

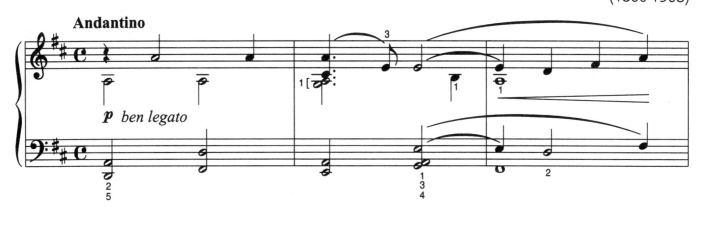

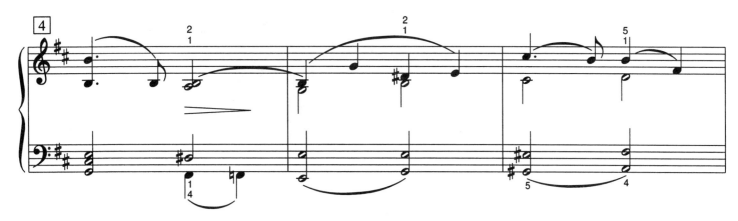

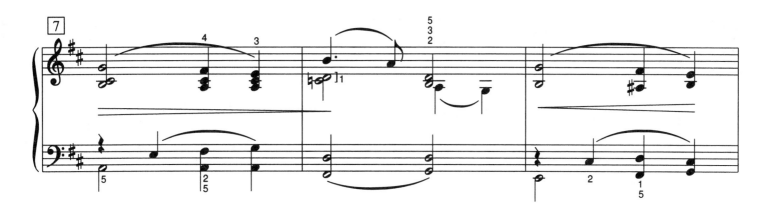

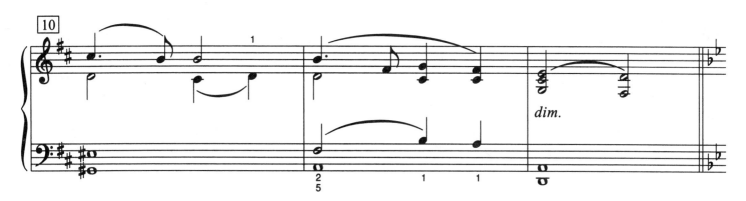

Tarantella

Op. 39, No. 2

Edward MacDowell
(1860-1908)

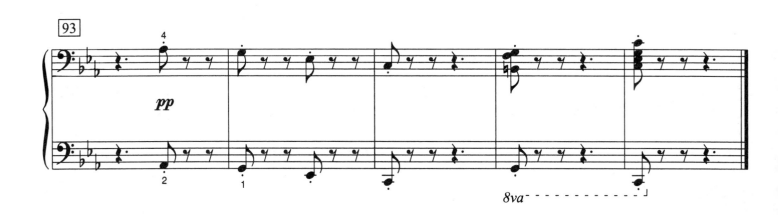